For my father, whose picture making first
inspired my own – MC

BIG PICTURE PRESS

First published in the UK in 2017 by Big Picture Press,
an imprint of Kings Road Publishing, part of the Bonnier Publishing Group,
The Plaza, 535 King's Road, London, SW10 0SZ
www.bonnierpublishing.com

1 3 5 7 9 10 8 6 4 2

ISBN 978-1-78370-814-7

This book was typeset in IM FELL Double Pica
and QumpellkaNo12
The illustrations were created with pen
and ink and coloured digitally

Consultant: Camilla de la Bedoyere
Designed by Helen Chapman
Written and edited by Katie Haworth

Printed in China

Animazes

Illustrated by Melissa Castrillón

BPP

Animal journeys

Many animals, both great and small, make incredible journeys.

Some, like reindeer, migrate to find food. Others, like Christmas Island red crabs, travel to find the right environment for the next generation to survive in.

Animals make journeys in water, by air, across arid deserts and over freezing pack ice. In *Animazes* you can follow the migrations of 14 very different creatures.

Can you find a safe path for every one?

How to use this book

Each maze in *Animazes* has a safe path to follow (as well as a few perilous dead ends. Be careful!). Trace the animal's journey with your finger and learn all sorts of fascinating facts along the way.

The beginning of each maze is marked with a start flag.

The end of each maze is marked with a finish flag.

In Animazes you will meet . . .

Christmas Island Red Crabs
These bright red crustaceans scuttle to the sea to lay their eggs.

Wildebeest
Huge herds of these creatures kick up the dust as they gallop across East Africa.

Humpback Whales
These mammals swim thousands of miles to give birth to their calves in the warm seas near the equator.

Reindeer
Vast herds of reindeer migrate to the Arctic tundra in summer.

Monarch Butterflies
One hundred million of these butterflies fly south to California and Mexico every winter.

Mali Elephants
These elephants travel to find water in the Sahara Desert.

Ruby-throated Hummingbirds
These tea-cup-sized birds make a dangerous journey over the Gulf of Mexico.

Alpine Ibexes
Acrobatic ibexes are cliff-hopping goats that migrate up mountains in summer.

Antarctic Krill
Tiny shrimp-like creatures, krill are an important food source for many animals.

Straw-coloured Fruit Bats
These bats swoop through Africa's midnight skies to find their favourite food.

Polar Bears
Polar bears migrate to follow their food source – seals – which swim amongst moving pack ice.

Rockhopper Penguins
These nimble penguins scale sheer cliffs to find a safe place for their eggs.

Sockeye Salmon
These champion swimmers swarm in rivers and can even jump up waterfalls!

Arctic Terns
These intrepid birds fly from the Arctic to Antarctica . . . and back again, every year.

Christmas Island Red Crabs

Christmas Island, in the Indian Ocean, is home to one of the most colourful migrations in the world. Every rainy season, the island's 40–50 million red crabs journey from the central rainforests to the coast where they mate and lay their eggs.

Migration begins when the monsoon rains arrive in around November.

Can you find the red crabs' path to the sea?

Crabs require moisture to survive. They stop migrating if the rains stop.

Cars are a major hazard to red crabs. Some roads on the island even have crab tunnels underneath.

It takes adult crabs around a week to get to the coast.

As soon at the crabs get to the sea they dip in the water to replenish fluids and salts.

The crabs mate in burrows near the coast. Males then return to the rainforests. Females wait 12–14 days until their eggs are ready.

Christmas Island is surrounded by tall cliffs Crabs can climb these steep surfaces.

The phase of the moon is important for red crab migration. Female crabs release eggs during the last quarter of the moon when the difference between high and low tides is smallest and they are less likely to be washed away.

The migration back to the rainforest takes young crabs around 9 days.

Male crabs begin the journey first. Females join slightly later.

Can you follow the baby crabs back to the rainforest?

Four weeks after the eggs hatch, tiny crabs with shells of 5mm (0.2in) emerge from the sea.

Female crabs stand on low cliffs and vibrate their bodies to flick their eggs into the sea. One crab can produce up to 100,000 eggs.

The larvae are a feast for predators like whale sharks. Millions are eaten and some years very few survive.

The eggs hatch into larvae, which go through several shrimp-like growth stages before they become tiny crabs.

Wildebeest are sensitive to changes in atmospheric pressure, and some scientists believe this is why they migrate towards storm clouds. Storms bring rain, meaning grass and water.

Wildebeest are preyed on by cheetahs, lions, hyenas and wild dogs.

Wildebeest begin migrating north between March and April.

Some 500,000 wildebeest calves are born every year. They can run 5 minutes after they are born.

Up to 450,000 Thomson's gazelle and 200,000 zebra migrate with the wildebeest.

By December–January, the herds have returned to their southern calving grounds.

Can you follow the wildebeest herds north?

Wildebeest

Wildebeest belong to the antelope family, but look more like small bison. Every year in the Serengeti Plain of East Africa, up to 1.3 million wildebeest migrate north. It is the largest mass migration of mammals on Earth.

The northern Serengeti, where wildebeest feed
September–October, has twice as much rain as the south.
It has trees and patches of forest.

Poachers kill
around 20,000
wildebeest a year.

Even in the green northern
Serengeti, wildebeest exhaust
food supplies quickly and
travel south again.

**Can you follow the herds
back to the south?**

In rivers, crocodiles
wait to snatch wildebeest
as they cross.

Serengeti
wildebeest travel up
to 3200km (2000mi)
a year.

The Mara River is fast and
dangerous after rains and
hundreds of wildebeest can be
drowned or crushed
in the water.

Many calves die in their first
year, especially if separated
from their mothers.

Humpback Whales

Humpback whales migrate from the Arctic and Antarctic waters, where they feed, to warm tropical waters where they have their young. Humpbacks can travel up to 9000km (5600mi) in a year – one of the world's longest mammal migrations.

Can you follow the whale to warmer water?

Humpbacks can eat up to 1.8 tonnes (2 tons) of krill a day.

In the final stages of the journey, whales eat little until they reach cold waters where krill is plentiful.

Whales can become tangled in fishing nets or be struck by ships, which may result in injury or death.

In summer, humpback whales feast on krill in colder waters to build up stores of body fat for their journey.

Whales begin their journey when falling temperatures drive krill to the seabed.

Some whales stop and rest on the return journey. Hervey Bay in eastern Australia is visited by mother whales and calves July–October.

The return journey is especially dangerous. Adult whales are weaker because they have used up body fat reserves.

Orca sometimes attack and kill humpback whales – especially young calves.

For whales, humpbacks are slow swimmers. Their fastest speed is 26kph (16mph), but their average is 3–14kph (2–9mph).

Once whales have reached warm waters near the equator, they give birth to their young and mate.

Can you follow the mother whale and calf back to the feeding grounds?

In May, the reindeer reach the grassy northern tundra, where they feed. They eat up to 5kg (11lb) of food a day.

North American reindeer have some of the longest journeys and may travel 4800km (3000mi) in a year.

Some nomadic peoples including the Nenets of Siberia migrate with the reindeer.

Migrating reindeer can run as fast as 80kph (50mph).

They travel in single file, standing in each other's hoof prints to avoid deep snow.

Reindeer head north at the beginning of spring, around March or April.

In winter, reindeer live in forests where they eat lichen. They dig this from under the snow with their scooped hooves.

Can you follow the reindeer to their summer grazing grounds?

Reindeer

Reindeer can be found in the northern regions of Europe, Russia and North America (where they are known as caribou). Every spring they migrate north to the meadows of the Arctic tundra where they feast on the nutritious new grasses that grow when winter snow melts.

All reindeer calves are born in a short, ten-day time period around June. This means that predators can take fewer calves.

Calves can run when they are only a day old.

Some reindeer cross rivers on their journey. These can be dangerous, but reindeer are good swimmers.

Can you follow the reindeer back to their winter range?

From September–October, reindeer begin the journey back to the south.

Arctic and grey wolves are the most dangerous predators to reindeer.

Once the reindeer return to their winter range, the annual migration cycle begins again.

Reindeer calves are also preyed on by golden eagles and bears.

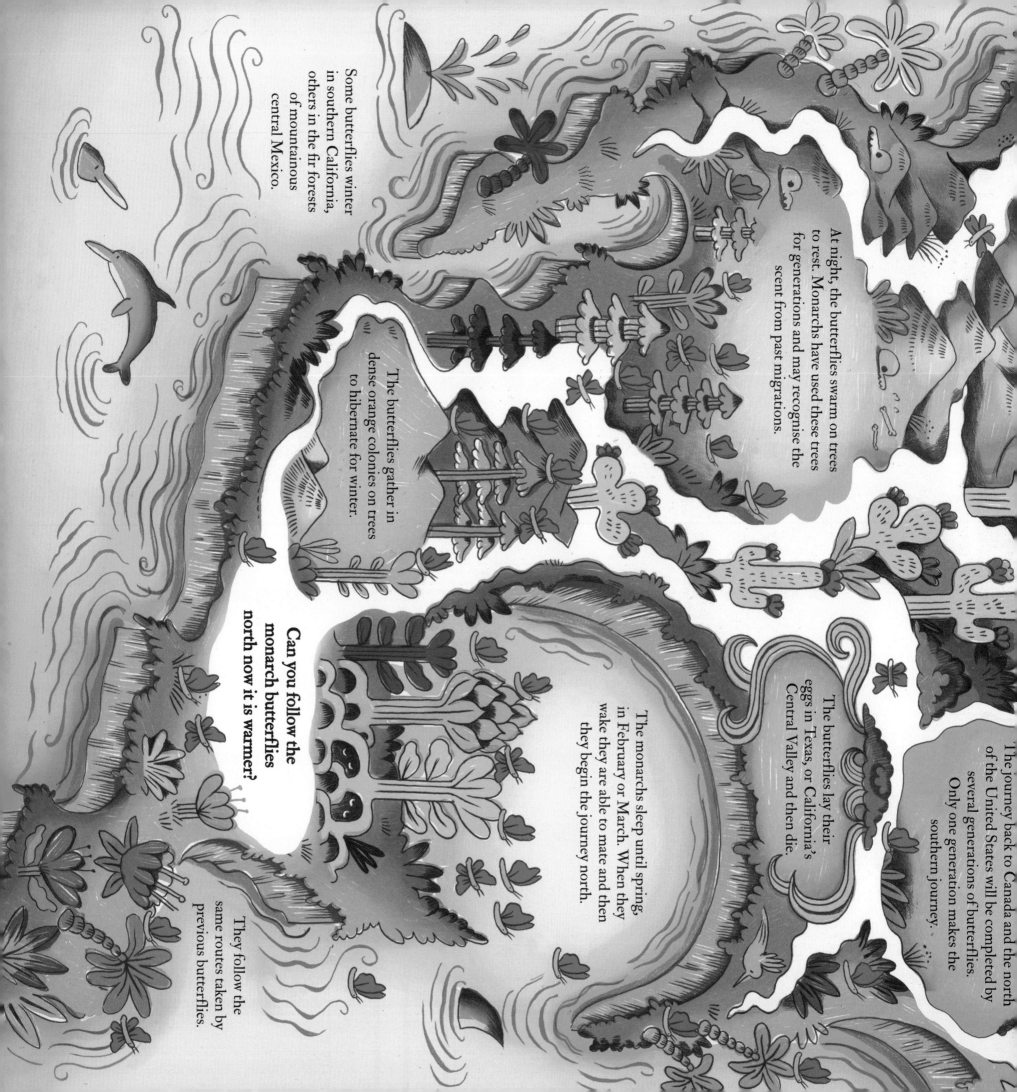

Some butterflies winter in southern California, others in the fir forests of mountainous central Mexico.

At night, the butterflies swarm on trees to rest. Monarchs have used these trees for generations and may recognise the scent from past migrations.

The butterflies gather in dense orange colonies on trees to hibernate for winter.

Can you follow the monarch butterflies north now it is warmer?

The butterflies lay their eggs in Texas, or California's Central Valley and then die.

The monarchs sleep until spring, in February or March. When they wake they are able to mate and then they begin the journey north.

The journey back to Canada and the north of the United States will be completed by several generations of butterflies. Only one generation makes the southern journey.

They follow the same routes taken by previous butterflies.

Monarch Butterflies

As winter approaches in North America, a black and orange cloud of more than 100 million monarch butterflies leaves the northern parts of the continent to fly south to Mexico and California. It is a migration of up to 5000km (3000mi) and several generations, for the butterflies that return north for summer will be the great grandchildren of those that migrated south.

The butterflies that migrate south do not have fully developed reproductive organs and will not lay eggs until after winter.

Before the butterflies migrate south they gorge on nectar to build up fat reserves.

Scientists believe butterflies start migrating due to autumn's shorter daylight hours and falling temperatures.

Can you follow the monarch butterflies south before winter?

In autumn, around late August, monarch butterflies start to head south.

Butterflies can travel around 130km (80mi) a day, or more if the winds are good.

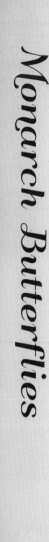

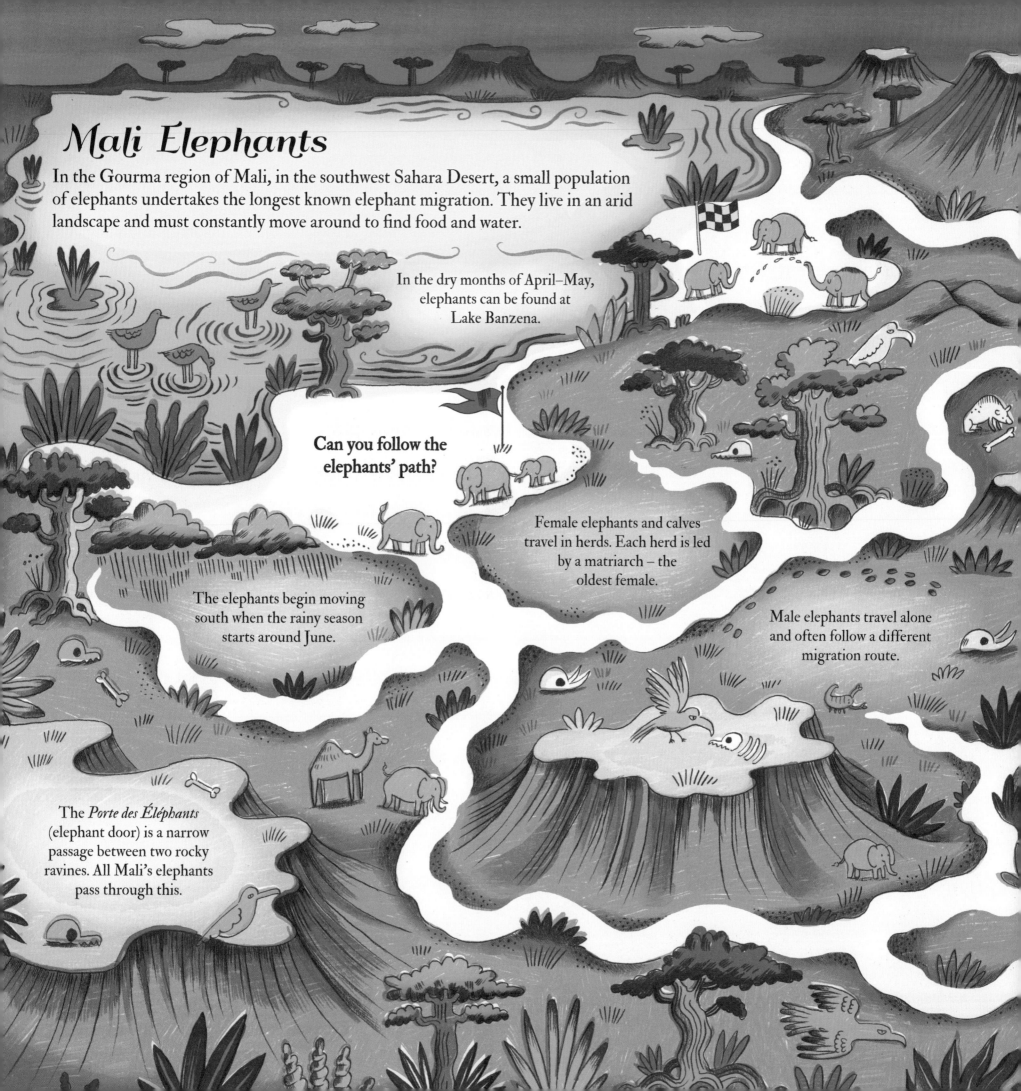

Mali Elephants

In the Gourma region of Mali, in the southwest Sahara Desert, a small population of elephants undertakes the longest known elephant migration. They live in an arid landscape and must constantly move around to find food and water.

In the dry months of April–May, elephants can be found at Lake Banzena.

Can you follow the elephants' path?

Female elephants and calves travel in herds. Each herd is led by a matriarch – the oldest female.

The elephants begin moving south when the rainy season starts around June.

Male elephants travel alone and often follow a different migration route.

The *Porte des Éléphants* (elephant door) is a narrow passage between two rocky ravines. All Mali's elephants pass through this.

Mali elephants can endure desert temperatures hotter than 50°C (122°F) by day.

Scientists believe there are around 350 Mali elephants left. They are the most northern herd of elephants in Africa.

Mali elephants are threatened by poachers, who illegally hunt the elephants for their ivory tusks.

In recent years, less rain and a growth in human population has increased competition for resources between humans and elephants.

They can travel up to 55km (34mi) a day, but these longer journeys usually happen at night when it is cooler.

Mali elephants migrate around 600km (370mi) a year. They usually travel around 10km (6mi) a day.

Around August, elephants cross into the nation of Burkina Faso. This is as far south as they will go.

Now it's the dry season and there isn't much water. Can you follow the elephants back to Lake Banzena?

Can you follow the hummingbirds south?

Females lay 1–3 pea-sized eggs, and feed their young for around 3 weeks.

Hawks, cats and even praying mantises can be threats to hummingbirds.

The birds fly south from around August to avoid the cold and scarcity of food that winter brings.

Young hummingbirds make thier first journey alone. Once they have learned a route they may follow it every year.

Fewer hummingbirds cross the Gulf of Mexico on the return journey, instead flying south along the coast of Texas.

In eastern North America, male birds put on a dramatic flying and diving display to attract a mate.

Some birds rest on fishing boats or oil rigs.

Ruby-throated hummingbirds winter in Mexico and Central America. Here the weather is warm and flowers bloom.

Many birds cross the Gulf of Mexico – a non-stop flight lasting 18–21 hours.

In January–February the hummingbirds head north. Males depart first, females a few weeks later.

Hummingbirds feast on insects and nectar before their migration. They can double their body weight.

Because hummingbirds are so small, strong winds and rain can be life-threatening.

Can you follow the hummingbirds' journey?

Ruby-throated Hummingbirds

With a wingspan of only 10cm (4in) and weighing only around 4g (0.14oz) – that's less than a pencil – these hummingbirds are some of the world's smallest long-distance travellers. Every year they make a 1600km (1000mi) journey across North America. Hummingbirds' wings beat up to 53 times a second, making a humming sound.

Straw-coloured fruit bats are large, powerful flyers with a wingspan of around 80cm (30in).

Many bats form colonies in treetops. These can be near waterfalls or loud city streets.

The bats leave their colonies between October and December.

Straw-coloured fruit bats are found in the tropical rainforests of sub-Saharan Africa.

A bat can make a round trip of 3800km (2400mi) in one year.

Can you follow the bats to Kasanka National Park?

Straw-coloured Fruit Bats

Every year, between October and December, 5–10 million straw-coloured fruit bats travel to Kasanka National Park in Zambia, southern Africa. The bats come to feast on the rainforest fruits, which ripen during the wet season.

In Kasanka National Park, 5–10 million bats gather between late October and December.

In the 'mushitu' swamp rainforests of Kasanka, the bats eat the abundant ripe fruit. They can eat twice their body weight in a night.

Bats can fly 90km (55mi) a night. They rest during the day.

Fruit bats play a vital role in the swamp forest ecosystem. They pollinate plants and disperse seeds.

The bats leave Kasanka around late December or early January when fruit is no longer available.

Alpine Ibexes

Alpine ibexes can be found in the mountain ranges of central Europe. In winter, they live lower in the mountains where there is less snow. As spring approaches they climb higher, to meadows and rocky slopes where they graze on the new plants that grow when the snow melts. This is known as 'altitudinal migration'.

Can you follow the alpine ibexes up the mountain?

In winter, alpine ibexes live at elevations as low as 1600m (5200ft).

...nutritious. Ibexes migrate up mountains to eat new spring growth.

By winter, ibexes have returned to lower elevations.

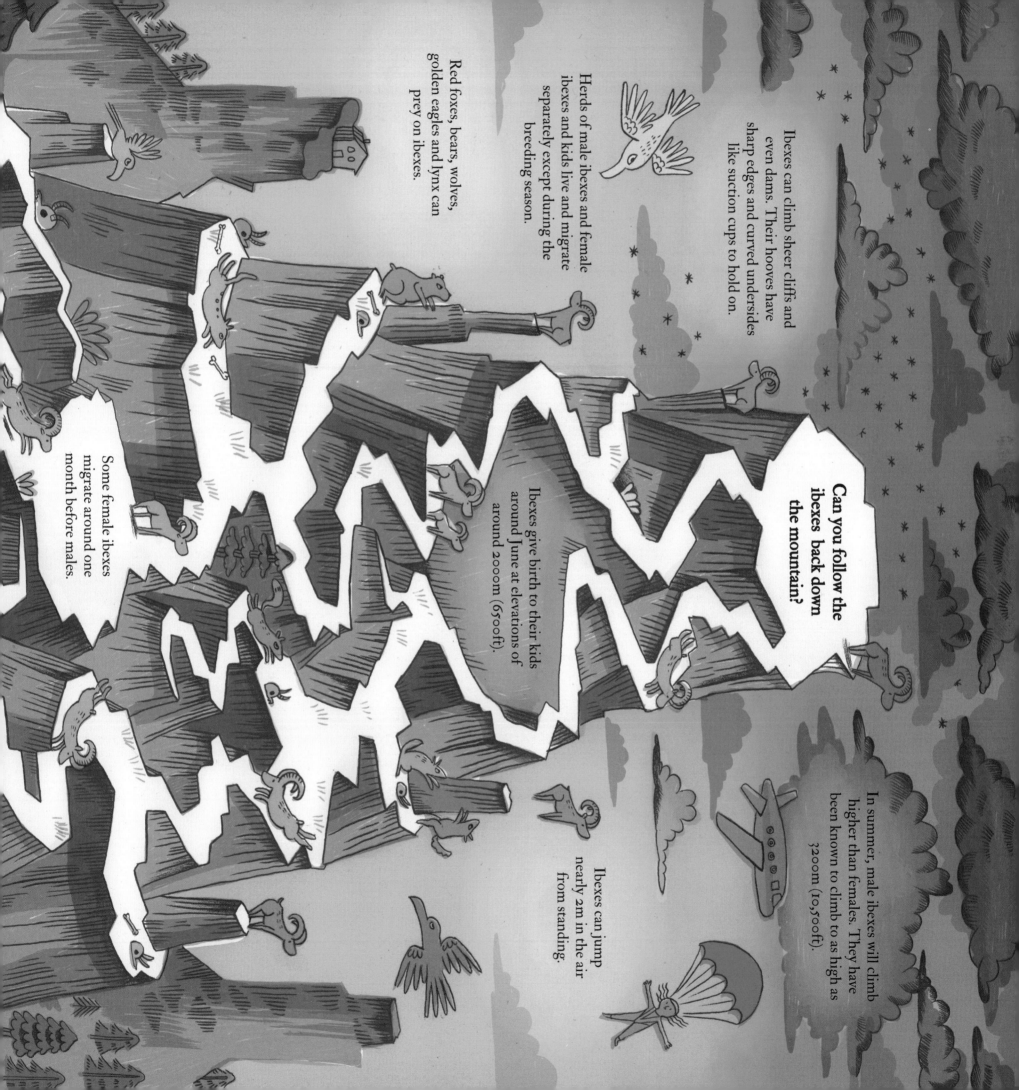

Ibexes can climb sheer cliffs and even dams. Their hooves have sharp edges and curved undersides like suction cups to hold on.

Herds of male ibexes and female ibexes and kids live and migrate separately except during the breeding season.

Red foxes, bears, wolves, golden eagles and lynx can prey on ibexes.

Some female ibexes migrate around one month before males.

Can you follow the ibexes back down the mountain?

Ibexes give birth to their kids around June at elevations of around 2000m (6500ft).

Ibexes can jump nearly 2m in the air from standing.

In summer, male ibexes will climb higher than females. They have been known to climb to as high as 3200m (10,500ft).

Antarctic Krill

Antarctic krill are tiny, shrimp-like creatures only around 5cm (2in) long, but they are the main food source for many animals. Krill are travellers with a difference – as well as migrating with the seasons, they rise and sink daily from the ocean's surface to deep beneath its waters.

Can you follow the krill swarm's seasonal journey?

Krill are the main food source for many Antarctic animals including whales, birds, seals and fish.

Krill larvae feed on algae found on the ice.

Between December and March, female krill lay their eggs. These sink 800–1000m (2600–3300ft).

Every winter, adult krill migrate from open water to the Antarctic coast. They often spend winter under pack ice.

Crabeater seals (despite their name) eat mainly krill, and their teeth have small points to filter krill from the water.

The huge blue whale can eat up to 3.6 tonnes (4 tons) of krill every day.

Once the larvae (immature form of krill) hatch from their eggs, they swim towards the water's surface.

Krill makes up around 95–99% of the diet of the chinstrap penguin.

Krill follow a daily migration cycle between the ocean's surface and deep water. This is called 'diel vertical migration' (DVM).

At night, krill feast on phytoplankton near the water's surface.

Can you follow the krill swarm's daily migration?

Krill are vital to the Southern Ocean ecosystem. They bring nutrients such as iron from deep water into the food cycle.

In summer, krill swarm to the open ocean to feed on phytoplankton (microscopic plants).

Krill return to surface waters about 12 hours after their descent, or when the sun sets.

Krill larvae live under pack ice during the winter.

Every 12 hours, or when the sun rises, krill swarms sink deep beneath the surface. This is to avoid predators.

Some krill migrate as deep as the ocean floor. Here they may eat iron-rich detritus.

Polar Bears

During winter, polar bears live on the edges of the frozen Arctic ice cap around the North Pole. In summer, when the pack ice breaks up, bears follow it as it drifts. Some even come ashore. During this time, polar bears can travel thousands of miles to find food.

Can you follow the polar bear south?

The bears hunt by waiting beside seals' breathing holes in the ice and pouncing when they emerge.

The flesh and blubber of ringed seals is polar bears' main food source. They also eat narwhals and walruses.

Polar bears can travel around 50km (31mi) a day.

They can swim long distances between sea ice, but may drown in storms.

When the ice floes break up in summer, polar bears travel for miles to follow the ice and stay with their food source.

Bears come ashore if the ice breaks down too much to follow.

Summer is a hungry time for polar bears. They may eat eggs, geese, plants or human rubbish – lean pickings for Earth's largest bear, which weighs up to 800kg (1750lb).

The polar bears that travel furthest are those that live the furthest south. In Hudson Bay, north Canada, bears come ashore every summer.

In winter, polar bears feast to build up stores of body fat for the summer migration ahead.

Climate change threatens the survival of polar bears, who rely on ice to hunt. Bears are around 80–90kg (180–200lb) lighter than they were 15 years ago.

Can you follow the polar bear back to the frozen north?

Polar bears can lose nearly 1kg (2lb) a day when fasting in summer.

Once there is enough ice, polar bears return north. Females in dens do not return until their cubs can travel.

In winter they usually hunt close to their colonies, but they may swim up to 2000km (1200mi) away.

Adult penguins can dive up to 100m (330ft) in search of food.

Around spring, the penguins swim back to their colonies. They return to the same colony every year.

Can you follow the penguins back to their colony?

The penguins can be eaten by leopard seals and fur seals.

They eat krill, squid and small fish.

The penguins spend the winter months foraging for food in the ocean. They can sleep at sea.

Rockhopper Penguins

Rockhopper penguins are some of the world's smallest. They spend 3–5 months at sea before gathering to breed on the bare, cliff-lined small islands north of Antarctica, from Chile to New Zealand.

They may be washed out to sea by waves and have to begin the climb again.

Can you follow the penguins up, then down the cliff?

Rockhopper penguins get their name from their ability to hop up the cliffs where they nest in spring.

The largest rockhopper penguin colony has more than 100,000 breeding pairs.

Female penguins lay eggs around November and they hatch a month later. Both parents care for the chick.

Penguins return to the oceans in early autumn. **Can you follow them?**

Sea birds like the brown skua prey on chicks. Rockhopper penguins protect their nests aggressively.

Sockeye Salmon

Sockeye salmon live in both the salty sea and in fresh water. They migrate from the Pacific Ocean up rivers in western North America and Kamchatka in Russia to breed. This journey can be as long as 2400km (1500mi). They find their way to rivers using ocean currents, sunlight and the Earth's magnetic field.

Can you follow the sockeye salmon to the lake?

Before sockeye salmon breed, they live in the Pacific Ocean. Their pink flesh comes from the krill they eat.

After 2–3 years in the sea, the salmon will return to the rivers. Most will go back to the same place they were spawned, which they recognise from the unique chemical make-up of its environment.

Human activity including fishing and the building of dams threatens salmon.

In late spring or early summer, salmon swarm up rivers.

Only 1–2% of smolts will make it back to the lakes and rivers as adults.

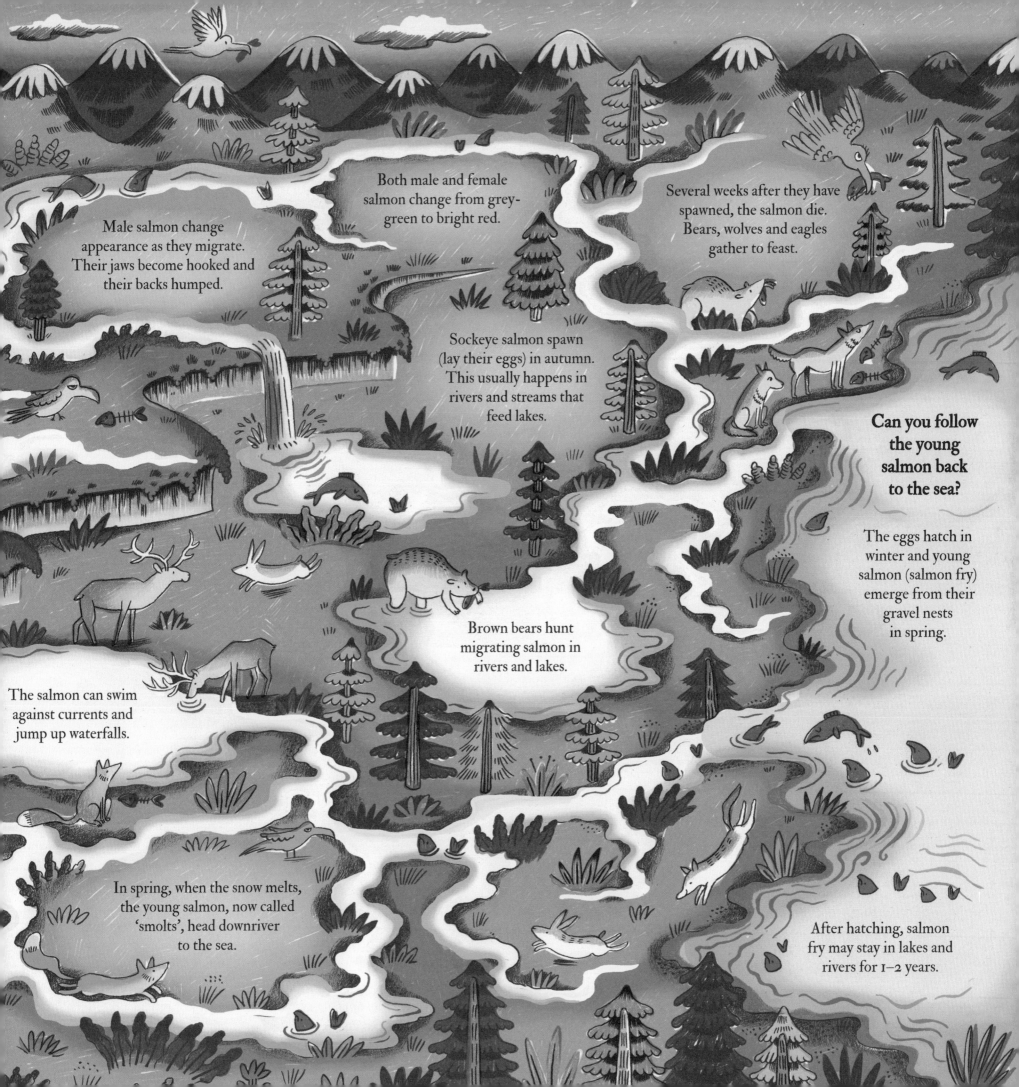

Male salmon change appearance as they migrate. Their jaws become hooked and their backs humped.

Both male and female salmon change from grey-green to bright red.

Several weeks after they have spawned, the salmon die. Bears, wolves and eagles gather to feast.

Sockeye salmon spawn (lay their eggs) in autumn. This usually happens in rivers and streams that feed lakes.

Can you follow the young salmon back to the sea?

The eggs hatch in winter and young salmon (salmon fry) emerge from their gravel nests in spring.

Brown bears hunt migrating salmon in rivers and lakes.

The salmon can swim against currents and jump up waterfalls.

In spring, when the snow melts, the young salmon, now called 'smolts', head downriver to the sea.

After hatching, salmon fry may stay in lakes and rivers for 1–2 years.

Arctic Terns

Arctic terns are small birds at only 34cm (13in) long, but they are extraordinary travellers. Every year, terns fly between the Arctic Circle and Antarctica, a journey of 20,000km (12,500mi) each way. This is one of the longest migrations on Earth. During its life a tern may travel 2.4 million km (1.5 million miles).

Can you help the Arctic terns fly south? There are 3 possible routes.

Terns that nest in and around Alaska fly south along the coast of the Pacific Ocean.

In the North and South Poles, the sun does not set in summer, when the terns are there. This means terns spend more time in sunlight than any animal.

In the middle of the north Atlantic Ocean, terns feast on zooplankton (tiny marine organisms) and small fish.

Terns can travel 390–670km (240–420mi) a day and can sleep while gliding.

The terns will stay around Antarctica for 4–5 months feasting on krill.

Adult terns leave Antarctica in early April. While the journey south can take around 90 days, the return journey takes only around 40. This is because the birds make use of different wind patterns.

Can you spot all the animals you've met in this book?

In July–August every year, terns begin their migration south. This journey takes around 90 days.

Terns that nest in Siberia, northern Europe, southeast Canada and Greenland, fly towards West Africa.

Choose a path.

Some birds fly south along Africa's coast, while others fly along the east coast of South America.

Terns weigh around only 110g (4oz). They can glide on the wind without flapping, which saves energy. They may be blown off course.

Answers

Did you find a safe path for every animal?

Christmas Island Red Crabs

Wildebeest

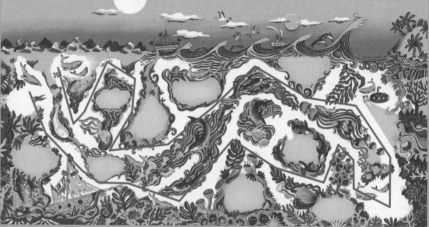

Humpback Whales

Reindeer

Monarch Butterflies

Mali Elephants

Ruby-throated Hummingbirds

Straw-coloured Fruit Bats

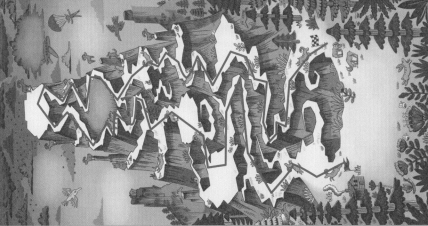

Alpine Ibexes

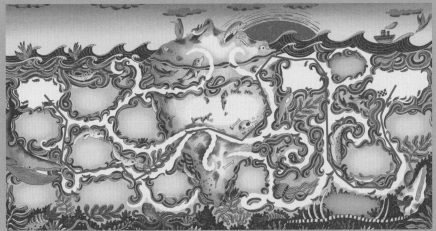

Antarctic Krill

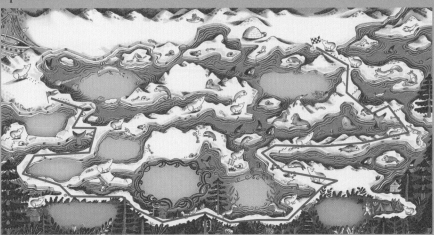

Polar Bears

Rockhopper Penguins

Sockeye Salmon

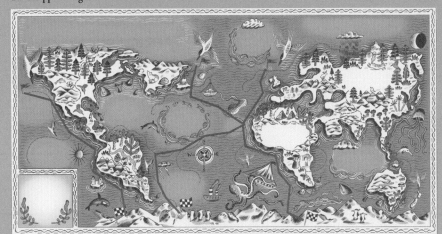

Arctic Terns